Written by Sue Graves
Illustrated by Jan Smith (Advocate)
Designed by Blue Sunflower Creative

Language consultant: Betty Root

This is a Parragon book
This edition published in 2007

Parragon
Queen Street House
4 Queen Street
Bath BA1 1HE, UK

ISBN 978-1-4054-9659-9
Printed in China

Where's Sparky?

A Level 4 Reading Book

p

Notes for Parents

Reading with your child is an enjoyable and rewarding experience. These **Gold Stars** reading books encourage and support children who are learning to read.

There are four different levels of reading book in the series. Within each level, the books can be read in any order. The steps between the levels are deliberately small because it is so important, at this early stage, for children to succeed. Success creates confidence.

Starting to read

Start by reading the book aloud to your child, taking time to talk about the pictures. This will help your child to see that pictures often give clues about the story.

6

Over a period of time, try to read the same book several times so that your child becomes familiar with the story and the words and phrases. Gradually, your child will want to read the book aloud with you. It helps to run your finger under the words as you say them.

Occasionally, stop and encourage your child to continue reading aloud without you. Join in again when your child needs help. This is the next step towards helping your child become an independent reader.

Finally, your child will be ready to read alone. Listen carefully to your child and give plenty of praise. Remember to make reading an enjoyable experience.

Using your Gold Stars stickers

You can use the **Gold Stars** stickers at the back of the book as a reward for effort as well as achievement. Learning to read is an exciting challenge for every child.

Remember these four important stages:

- Read the story **to** your child.
- Read the story **with** your child.
- Encourage your child to read **to you.**
- Listen to your child read **alone.**

This is Charlie. Charlie is in Miss Jolly's class. Miss Jolly is his teacher.

Miss Jolly's class

One day Miss Jolly had a surprise for everyone.

"We're going on a visit to the fire station," she said. "We will go in a bus."

"Hurray!" said everyone.

Everyone got ready.

"You must all choose a partner," said Miss Jolly. "You must stay with your partner all the time at the fire station."

Charlie chose Frankie to be his partner.

Then Miss Jolly picked up a big box.

"All our lunches are in this box," she said.
"We will eat them after our visit."

At the fire station they met Mr Finn.
Mr Finn was a fire fighter.

"Hello, everyone," said Mr Finn. "I am Mr
Finn and this is my cat Sparky. Sparky
follows me everywhere but he can be a bit
naughty sometimes."

Hello, everyone.

"You must all be very good and not naughty like Sparky," said Miss Jolly to the children. "A fire station can be a very dangerous place."

Mr Finn told them about the fire station. It had lots of rooms. He showed them the rest room. The rest room had lots of chairs in it.

He showed them the kitchen, too. The
kitchen had lots of cupboards in it.

Mr Finn let them do
lots of things, too.

He let them slide
down the pole.

He let them sit in the big fire engine. He
even let them sound the siren.

Nee-naw! Nee-naw!

Then Mr Finn let Charlie put on a fire fighter's helmet.

"Oh wow!" said Charlie. "I wish I was a fire fighter. I wish I could rescue someone."

Everyone was good at the fire station. But Sparky was naughty. First he ran round and round the fire station.

Then he dug in the sand bucket.

Next he sat in a fire fighter's helmet. Last of all he tangled himself up in the hose.

Meow!

"Oh dear," said Mr Finn. "Sparky can be such a naughty cat. None of you must be naughty like him. A fire station can be a dangerous place!"

Soon it was time to go home.

"Everyone, find your partners," said Miss Jolly.

Everyone found their partners.

"Oh dear," said Mr Finn. "I can't find Sparky. Has anyone seen him?"

They all shook their heads.

"We haven't seen Sparky at all," they said. "But we will help you look for him."

I can't find Sparky.

"We must find Sparky quickly," said Mr Finn. "A fire station can be a dangerous place."

They all looked in the rest room. They looked behind the chairs.

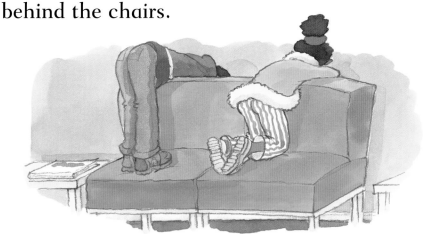

They looked under the chairs. But they could not find Sparky.

Then they looked in the kitchen. They looked under the cupboards.

They looked in the cupboards. But Sparky wasn't there either.

"Where can he be?" said Miss Jolly.

Then Charlie had an idea.

"The only place we haven't looked for Sparky is on our bus," he said. "I wonder if Sparky is there?"

"We'd better go and look," said Mr Finn.

They all went to the bus.

"I can't see Sparky," said Miss Jolly. "Where can he be?"

Just then Charlie heard a noise. It was coming from a box on the seat.

"I think I have found Sparky," said Charlie. He pulled open the box. Sparky was inside.

"Oh, Sparky," laughed Miss Jolly. "You wanted our lunches."

"Yes," said Charlie. "But then he must have got stuck in the box."

"Well, it was lucky that Charlie came to your rescue," said Mr Finn. "Hurray for Charlie!"

"Hurray!" shouted everyone.

Mr Finn gave Sparky a big hug. "And perhaps now you won't be so naughty," he laughed.

Answer these questions. Look back in the book to find the answers.

What was the
teacher's name?

Who was Mr Finn?

What was the cat's name?

Where did everyone look for Sparky first?

Where did everyone look for Sparky next?

Now re-tell the story in your own words.

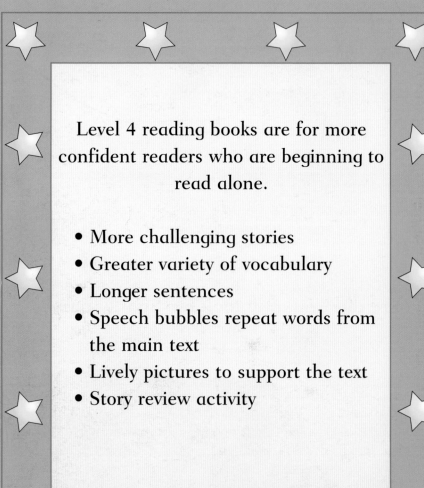

Level 4 reading books are for more confident readers who are beginning to read alone.

- More challenging stories
- Greater variety of vocabulary
- Longer sentences
- Speech bubbles repeat words from the main text
- Lively pictures to support the text
- Story review activity